Fantastic!
No more plastic...

Written by Nigel Green

Illustrated by Debbie Martin

Published by IM Books

Fantastic! No more plastic...

ISBN 978-1-5262-0865-1

To the most important women in my life
Jenny, Julia, Emily, Annabel and Olivia.

Special thanks to Julia for her advice and guidance
and Olivia, my granddaughter, for the incentive to
write this book.

Destiny was a dolphin... but she was a sad dolphin.

She had a very tickly nose. Plastic made it tickle.

Eli was an electric eel... but he was a sad eel.
He crackled and sparked. Plastic made him crackle.

Because Destiny and Eli sneezed and crackled, they had no friends. Every day they would swim around in the sea full of plastic, sneezing and crackling and sparking.

3

But one day they bumped into each other. Destiny sneezed
and blew Eli into a bubble, but he didn't mind.
He just popped the bubble and they carried on.

They were different but they became friends.
That was all that mattered.

One day, whilst swimming and playing, they saw a tropical island. It was called ITSAFATTYPOOEY. There were lots of children splishing and splashing near the beach.

After a while the children saw Destiny and Eli watching.
The children were really friendly and they let
Destiny and Eli play with them.

6

But with all the plastic around, Destiny's nose started to tickle and tickle. "I'm going to sneeze!" she said. "Oh no!" said Eli. "Take cover!"

He tried to cover Destiny's nose, but something strange happened when they touched. Destiny sneezed and Eli crackled and then...

There was a babbling and a bubbling...
There was a whizzing and a fizzing...

There was a splashing
and a spraying...

And then a humming and
a buzzing...

The sea sparkled and then...

... all the plastic that was on the beach - straws, shopping bags, bottles, fish netting, started moving.

It made a thumping, wumping, lumping, dumping sound - and stuck to Destiny's nose!

What had happened?

Then Destiny had an idea...

"That's what happens when you have special friends!"

The children laughed and were very happy too.

They were delighted to see the sea so clean again.

The next day Destiny and Eli visited another island.
It was also surrounded by plastic rubbish.

Again, Destiny's nose tickled and tickled and Eli tried to
stop Destiny's sneeze but... well you've guessed it...

There was a babbling and a bubbling, a whizzing
and a fizzing, a splashing and a spraying...
And then a humming and a buzzing...

The sea sparkled and then all the plastic on the beach went
thump, wump, lump, dump onto Destiny's nose again!

NEWS EVERYWHERE

Destiny and Eli SAVE THE WORLD!

When Destiny first sneezed and Eli crackled, little did they know they were going to save the world...

But they did!

Soon grown-ups heard about Destiny and Eli, and they became very famous. They travelled everywhere to help...

And it worked everywhere! Destiny and Eli even made up a little song to sing about it.

To the tune of "Twinkle, twinkle little star..."

Plastic, plastic in the sea,
it needs clearing very quickly.
Bright and sparkling is what we wish,
for all the dolphins, crabs and fish!

Pick it up and put it away,
not just now but every day.
Soon we'll all be able to say,
"No more plastic, hip, hip, hooray!"

Everyone loved Destiny and Eli. They'd helped clear the seas and beaches from plastic. Children now had lots of nice clean places to splash and play.

But there was still one problem...

What to do with all the plastic once it was collected?
So, the grown-ups built a ship to change the plastic into
something safe for the world and the seas.

Changing the plastic was called recycling, and the ship was called Michael.

My name is Michael, and I like to recycle.

I am a solution to no more pollution.

So put the plastic in my mouth or any bucket or bin.

Not just once, but all the time,

And very soon the world will be just fine!

Thanks to Destiny and Eli the earth was a great place to live again. For everyone it was absolutely...

FANTASTIC! THERE WAS NO MORE PLASTIC!

But Destiny and Eli can't get to every beach in the world all the time, so....

They have asked if everyone who goes to the seaside could pick up a piece of plastic from the beach.

If everyone does this, it won't take long for all the beaches and seas to become clean, and very soon...

It WILL be fantastic,

there'll be no more plastic!

About the Author...

Nigel Green is passionate about nature and having watched David Attenborough's Blue Planet he was devastated to see the extent of plastic pollution in the seas and how it was affecting marine life.

His opinion? As it's all our fault, it's up to us to put it right! By educating everyone now, we will hopefully leave a planet fit for future generations.

With only a little effort and plenty of consideration we can all start to help Destiny and Eli by:
RECYCLING everything you can at home, at school, everywhere – just look at the label.

At Home
*All cardboard and all plastic bottles can be recycled. In fact, glass can be recycled endlessly – so use glass instead of plastic wherever you can.
*Try to fix things rather than replace them.

At School
*Use the recycling bins for your rubbish.
*Take packed lunches in re-usable containers and water in re-usable water bottles
*Reduce the use of paper and recycle it when you do use it.

When out
*Don't buy drinks – take them with you.
*Take re-usable shopping bags with you.

Remember RE-USE bottles, shopping bags, rainwater, face masks, food containers, bottles.
Remember wood is good... plastic is nasty, and as you know, plastic straws suck!

Printed in Great Britain
by Amazon

67821147R00017